SURVIVING
on the foods and water from Alaska's southern shores

Dolly A. Garza

Marine Advisory Program
University of Alaska
Sitka, Alaska

MAB-38 • Price $4.00

Elmer E. Rasmuson Library Cataloging-in-Publication Data

Garza, Dolly A.

Surviving on the foods and water from Alaska's southern shores

(MAB-38)

1. Survival skills—Alaska. 2. Wilderness survival—Alaska. I. Alaska Sea
Grant College Program. II. Title. III. Series: Marine advisory bulletin ; no. 38.

GF86.G37 1989

Second Printing 1998

ISBN 1-56612-056-X

Credits

Editing by Sue Keller, layout by Karen Lundquist, Alaska Sea Grant. Illustra-
tions by Ben Swan, Rene Patton, and Karen Lundquist.

Published by the University of Alaska Sea Grant College Program, which is
cooperatively supported by the U.S. Department of Commerce, NOAA
Office of Sea Grant, grant no. NA46RG-0104, project A/75-01; and by the
University of Alaska with state funds. The University of Alaska is an affirma-
tive action/equal opportunity employer and educational institution.

Sea Grant is a unique partnership with public and private sectors combining
research, education, and technology transfer for public service. This national
network of universities meets changing environmental and economic needs
of people in our coastal, ocean, and Great Lakes regions.

University of Alaska Sea Grant
P.O. Box 755040
Fairbanks, Alaska 99775-5040
fypubs@uaf.edu
Phone (907) 474-6707 Fax (907) 474-6285
http://www.uaf.edu/seagrant/

Cover: Small perennial kelp, a tasty seaweed. Like most seaweeds, it is
edible and contains about 2.85 calories per gram. Cover design by Dave
Brenner, photo by Kurt Byers, Alaska Sea Grant.

TABLE OF CONTENTS

Introduction

Knowledge of the contents of this booklet will be useful to fishermen, recreational boaters, hikers, and other travelers who risk getting lost along Alaska's coast south of Kodiak. The information presented here is unique in that it covers both land and sea resources available for survival.

In a survival situation wild edible plants and animals may be the mainstay of your diet. While most people in need of rescue are found within 48 to 72 hours, rescue is not guaranteed and some people have spent days and weeks in a survival situation. Thus some knowledge of local wild foods is recommended.

For optimum personal performance during the wait for rescue, the two most important essentials are (1) to consume adequate amounts of water and (2) to attempt balanced nutrition by eating as wide a variety of available foods as possible.

It is important to know safe sources of local wild foods. Putting up local foods for home consumption provides an excellent opportunity to learn cooking methods for various food resources. Learning through experience far outweighs learning from a book. Caution should be taken while learning to preserve local foods, as there are several poisonous and unpalatable plants and animals. By learning which plants and animals are safe to eat and which may be dangerous, you are preparing yourself to survive on wild foods should you need to.

Knowing and understanding the nutritional content of various foods is not critical for short-term survival. However, if you know nutritional values of and cooking methods for wild foods, you will be better prepared to collect and eat nutritious foods if you become lost without supplies for a longer period.

Requirements of the Human Body

In a survival (or any) situation, nutrients are essential for

- energy for activity or heat
- resistance to infection and disease
- tissue repair
- brain power and proper mental functioning
- comfort and a feeling of well-being
- body process regulation

Factors that affect daily nutritional needs include stress, work, exposure to the environment, and personal metabolism.

The six groups of nutrients essential to proper body functioning are

- water
- carbohydrates
- fats `
- proteins
- vitamins
- minerals

Water is vital for almost all body functions including metabolism and digestion. Carbohydrates, fats, and proteins are sources of energy for the body, supplying necessary fuel for body heat and work. Vitamins and minerals are important in small quantities.

In a survival situation, securing a safe source of drinking water is the most important nutritional requirement. Our bodies can go for weeks without food but only days without water. Knowing several safe plants and animals to eat during every season is the second most important requirement. Finally, you should know which plants and animals are poisonous and should be avoided.

Local Sources of Water and Edible Foods

Alaska has a multitude of land and water plants and animals. While it is possible to live off these resources, you must first acquire an understanding for the edible and non-edible or poisonous plants and animals. If you familiarize yourself with the local resources by harvesting and eating them, you will be better prepared to satisfy your food and nutrient requirements in a survival situation.

While some of these resources may seem unappetizing, remember the Native peoples of Alaska have lived off these resources for thousands of years. During this time, experience served as the educator for safe and unsafe foods, as well as preservation methods. Many of these resources are still collected today for food consumption and are preserved using age-old methods.

Water

Water is the most abundant and important nutrient accounting for approximately two-thirds of the total weight of the body. Water is involved in nearly every body process including digestion, absorption, circulation, and excretion.

On the average, the body needs three quarts of water per day depending on activities. A sedentary person may use only one quart per day while an active person may use up to ten quarts per day. Water is

Debris such as cans and plastic can be used for collecting rain water. D. Garza photo.

lost through body waste removal, respiration, and perspiration.

If you continue to function without re-supplying your body with water, you will become dehydrated. Severe dehydration can result in death.

Symptoms of dehydration include

- thirst (an initial sign)
- headache (an initial sign)
- dark urine
- craving for cold wet foods
- chapped lips and dry skin
- nausea
- dull mental function
- leg cramps
- depression (a killer in a survival situation)

Water sources include lakes, streams, springs, rain, snow, ice, and bogs. However, ground water can be contaminated with minerals, microorganisms, and chemicals.

Giardia or "beaver fever" is the most serious illness caused by organisms in contaminated water—severe cases have even resulted in death. Symptoms include a vague feeling of physical discomfort, cramps, excessive gas, and abdominal bloating. The symptoms of this disease may not show up for several weeks, a period longer than the average length of a survival situation. Dysentery, on the other hand, which results in abdominal cramps and intense diarrhea, strikes within hours after contaminated water is consumed.

Safe sources of water include rain water collected in a clean container, water that has been through a pump-activated filter, water boiled for 20 minutes, or prepackaged drinking water.

All ground-collected water should be considered contaminated and should be boiled for 20 minutes to ensure that all microorganisms are killed. Water boiled for one minute will be free of giardia cysts but will not be 100 percent free of bacteria and viruses that may cause dysentery or other illness. If your heat source is limited, you will need to consider this fact.

Store-bought chemicals such as household bleach, two percent iodine, and water treatment tablets may be used but they are not 100 percent effective in killing microorganisms.

Containers to collect and boil water can be hard to find if you are without supplies. Plastic, metal, bark, leaves, and shells can be used for collecting water. Boiling water in some of these containers is tricky and prior practice may be necessary.

Use your body as your water receptacle by drinking enough to quench your thirst. It is better to prevent sweating as much as possible than to ration your water consumption. Minimizing your body water loss can be accomplished by confining your activities to those necessary for survival.

Do not drink urine or salt water, which may make you sick. Urine contains harmful waste products and a high concentration of salt. Seawater can lead to dehydration.

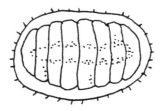

A gumboot, or chiton, has a shell of overlapping plates.
The largest chitons in southeastern Alaska are 10 inches long.

Proteins

Proteins are important for growth, development, and repair of body tissues and organs. The easiest proteins to obtain include fish, shellfish, and small game. Avoid hunting for large animals because you can waste a lot of time and energy stalking something you may not be successful in bagging.

Sea animals that you might find during low tide include limpets, small snails, abalone, chiton or gumboots, blennies (eel-like fish), small crabs, sea cucumbers, and small- to medium-size octopus. Fish such as small flounder or rockfish can be caught near shore. Most intertidal animals are found throughout the year and are easily collected. The protein contents and species for some of the sea animals you may find are listed in Table 1 of the Appendix.

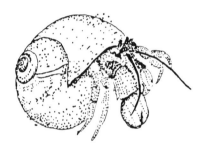

Hermit crabs carry a snail shell with them as their home.
These small crabs can provide needed protein.

Carbohydrates

Carbohydrates include sugar, starch, and fiber. Plants are an excellent source of carbohydrates. Carbohydrates may be found in the berry, the leaf, the stalk, and the root.

Numerous plants are edible and nutritious. The more widely distributed species include wild rose hips, salmonberries, cloudberries, currants, cranberries, blueberries, sourdock, fireweed, goosetongue, Labrador tea, beach greens, and the fiddleheads and roots of some ferns. Nutritional values and species of several plants are given in Table 2 of the Appendix.

Seaweeds also contain significant amounts of carbohydrates and proteins, although some of the carbohydrates are not digestible by

Blennies (long, narrow fish) and sea cucumbers are good sources of protein.
The sea cucumber is about the size of a cucumber pickle. D. Garza photo.

All sea urchins are edible. The eggs, a source of fat, can be scooped out
of the shell with a finger and eaten raw. J. Doyle photo.

humans. Seaweeds such as the bull kelp and several of the brown kelps can be found year-round. However, many of the seaweeds including the black seaweed, sea lettuce, and dulse are seasonal and harvested during late spring or early summer. Nutritional values and species of several seaweeds are listed in Table 3 of the Appendix.

Fats

Fats are the most concentrated source of energy in the diet, providing over twice as much energy as carbohydrates and proteins. Sources of fat include sea urchin gonads, bird eggs and meat, some fish eggs, and fatty fish including cod, herring, and salmon. Several of these animals may be difficult to harvest in a survival situation, however.

Few shellfish or intertidal life have significant levels of fat; thus fat may be a limited staple in a survival diet. Proteins and carbohydrates should provide needed energy.

Vitamins and Minerals

Vitamins and minerals are important in small quantities for metabolism, to help maintain the integrity of the skeletal system, and to serve

Bull kelp is a source
of vitamins and minerals.

as catalysts in biochemical reactions in the body. By consuming a wide variety of foods you will insure intake of both vitamins and minerals essential to various body processes.

Seaweeds are good sources of vitamin A, vitamin C, the vitamin B complex, niacin, and calcium (Table 2 of Appendix), as well as iodine. The large and flat brown, red, and green seaweeds are all safe and can be eaten raw, cooked, or dried. Local edible and nutritious seaweeds include black seaweed, ribbon seaweed, fucus, alaria, laminaria, bull kelp, and sea lettuce. The vitamin and mineral content of these seaweeds is highest in spring and summer.

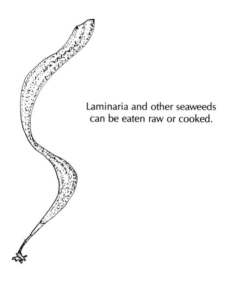

Laminaria and other seaweeds can be eaten raw or cooked.

Most berries and greens have a fair amount of vitamins C and A (see Table 3 in Appendix). Excellent sources for vitamin C include rose hips, fireweed, cloudberries, cranberries, sourdock, willow shoots and leaves, and most seaweeds. Local sources of vitamin A include beach asparagus, fern fiddleheads, and sourdock.

Good sources for the vitamin B complex, important for dealing with stress, are herring eggs, sea cucumbers, gumboots, crab, trout, black seaweed, bull kelp, alaria, fireweed, fern fiddleheads, and sourdock (see Tables 1-3 in Appendix).

Iron can be found in good supply in the seaweeds, gumboots, eulachon, and octopus.

Preparation of Wild Foods

There are several general rules for preparing foods in a survival situation.

Seaweeds and almost all sea animals should be rinsed well in clean fresh water to minimize salt intake. One of the few exceptions to this rule is sea urchin gonads, which become mushy in fresh water. The gonads are eaten raw, or the entire animal can be laid on a bed of coals for a while to cook the gonads. The gonads also can be fried. Edible leaves and berries can be eaten raw or cooked. Roots are better boiled or roasted. Seaweeds can be eaten raw, boiled, or dried.

Shellfish can be eaten raw, boiled, or placed on rocks near a fire to cook in their own shell. Fish should not be eaten raw. It can be boiled, or it can be roasted by wrapping in skunk cabbage leaves or brown seaweed and placing it on rocks near a fire.

Seasonal Menus

All-Season Survival Chowder
Survival chowder is an all-season nutritious and easy meal to fix using small intertidal animals such as limpets, snails, and seaweeds.

Boil fresh water for 15 minutes. Throw in seafoods and boil for 5 more minutes. The meat from the limpets and snails will separate from the shells. The water will be filled with vitamins and minerals.

Optional: Small fish added to the stew will contribute fat, and edible leaves or roots will contribute carbohydrates.

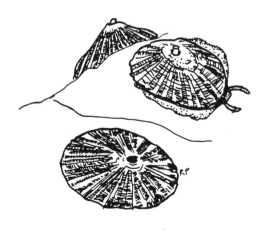

Limpets can be pried from rocks with a knife, and eaten raw or cooked.

9

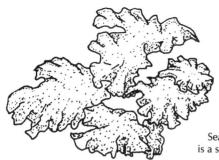

Sea lettuce, bright green and tissue thin, is a source of vitamins for the shore survivor.

Spring (March-May)
  Escargot (small snails)—steamed
  Fern fiddleheads—steamed
  Eulachon—boiled
  Chickweed, willow, and fireweed greens—tossed raw
  Herring eggs on kelp
  Seaweeds: ribbon, black, or sea lettuce—raw (rinse first)
  Fireweed—steeped in hot water for tea

Summer (June-August)
  Gumboots—boiled for five minutes
  Sea cucumbers—steamed or baked
  Goosetongue and beach asparagus—steamed
  Chickweed—raw as salad
  Seaweeds: ribbon, brown, fucus, bull kelp—raw (rinse first)
  Salmonberries, blueberries, huckleberries—mix, for dessert

Fall (September-November)
  Flatfish or blennies—boiled or steamed
  Fern root—baked
  Survival chowder—see above; add Indian rice (bulbs of chocolate
      lily or *Fritillaria camschatcensis*)
  Cranberries, currants, huckleberries—mix for dessert
  Labrador tea leaves and rose hips—steep in hot water for tea

Winter (December-February)
  Survival chowder—add Indian rice
  Sea urchin roe
  Wild potato (silverweed or *Potentilla anserina* root) and fern
      root—baked
  Labrador tea leaves—steep in hot water for tea

Goosetongue leaves, picked when they are six to eight inches long,
are a nutritious addition to the summer survival stew. D. Garza photo.

Fucus, a brown seaweed, can be eaten raw or added to the summer survival stew.
D. Garza photo.

11

All-Season Foods
  Gumboots
  Limpets
  Snails
  Blennies
  Octopus
  Brown seaweeds

Non-Edible Animals and Plants

Paralytic Shellfish Poisoning

All of the bivalve shellfish (shellfish with two shells) may contain the toxin that causes paralytic shellfish poisoning (PSP), hence are unsafe to eat in the wilderness. PSP is caused by a dinoflagellate with an extremely potent neurotoxin that blocks nerve impulses. It eventually can result in death due to respiratory failure.

Bivalves to avoid include all clams, cockles, mussels, scallops, oysters, and geoduck. In addition, filter-feeding barnacles and clam-eating moon snails have tested positive for this toxin. PSP toxin levels are different for each bivalve, and the duration of the toxicity varies. Mussels can be very toxic when the toxin is present and as little as one mussel can kill a person. The toxin may be cleaned out of the mussel's system within weeks. Butter clams, on the other hand, are toxic for several years after they ingest the toxin.

Clams and other bivalves should not be eaten in a survival situation, because they may cause paralytic shellfish poisoning. Photo courtesy of Alaska Marine Safety Education Association.

Even if you eat clams or other bivalves at home, do not eat them in a survival situation. If you get PSP from eating clams at home, you may be close to medical help. However, if you are out in the wilderness medical help will not be available and you will likely die after eating toxic clams. Symptoms of PSP will start between 5 and 30 minutes after eating, although it can be longer. A tingling or burning sensation around the lips, gums, and tongue is felt, followed by a prickly feeling or numbness in the fingers and toes. This sensation may spread within four to six hours through the arms, legs, and neck. Drowsiness, incoherence of speech, impaired vision, headache, staggering, and respiratory problems may follow. Without proper medical attention, death will occur from respiratory failure.

Sea Animals

The hairy triton, a greenish deep-water snail with small brown fuzzy hairs on it, should be avoided. Since it is a deep-water species, you probably will not find it on the shore.

The starfish, coral, sea anemone, jellyfish, sponge, nudibranch, and sand dollar may have light toxins that they use to catch their prey. They have little or no nutritional value and should be avoided.

Sculpin or bullhead eggs are poisonous. The armored sea cucumber has an unpalatable odor when raw or cooked.

Plants

Several of Alaska's plants are poisonous or inedible, and it is important to know the plants you are considering for food. If you are not sure, do not eat them. Look for available sources to learn the local

Poisonous water hemlock is a deadly poisonous plant found in marshy areas.

13

plants and their edibility. Several of the poisonous species of plants look similar to edible species.

Some toxic land plants are baneberry, wild sweet pea, water hemlock, narcissus-flowered anemone, nutka lupine, vetch, false hellebore, and death camas. To the untrained eye the poisonous water hemlock looks similar to the edible and delicious wild celery and easily can be confused with it.

Learn the description, habitat, and toxicity of these plants. There may be plants in your area that are toxic raw but safe after being prepared properly. Be sure you know plants before eating them. Look for books and other materials that cover the edible plants in your area or take a class on local edible plants. Several useful books and pamphlets are listed in the reference section of this booklet.

Two seaweeds to avoid include *Desmarestia ligulata* and *Corallina vancouveriensis*. This *Corallina* is a small, hard, bright pink alga and often is found growing on abalone or other shellfish in exposed waters. Because the alga looks like a coral and is small, it is unlikely that it would be used as a survival food.

Desmarestia ligulata is a large brown branch-like seaweed that is found in the lower part of the intertidal zone. When it is taken out of the water it turns green. It is not recommended for eating, because sulfuric acid is released when the plant is damaged or handled.

Mushrooms should be avoided, since several species in Alaska are poisonous. Although some are a good source of minerals, most have little nutritional value.

The roots and red or white fruits
of the baneberry are very poisonous.

Summary

Becoming familiar with the edible and non-edible land plants, sea-weeds, and sea animals is a must for anyone who spends time in the out-of-doors and risks getting stranded in the wilderness without provisions. Tables 1-3 of the Appendix list some plants and animals you can eat in the wilderness, and the reference section lists publications you can use to learn others. Learn about the edibles by trying them in your home, since this will improve your chances of surviving in an emergency.

This booklet gives basic information on nutritional needs of the human body and some wilderness sources to meet those needs. Water intake is most important to the body, and all surface water must be purified before drinking. Sea animals from the intertidal zone are good sources of protein, and land plants are the best sources of carbohydrates. Fats are found in eggs of birds and sea animals, as well as in fish. Seaweeds and the berries and leaves of land plants provide many of the essential vitamins and minerals.

Some of the wild foods can be eaten raw and others can be prepared by boiling, steaming, or baking. In a survival situation, the season limits the foods and thus limits the recipes.

All bivalves should be avoided in the wilderness because of the possibility of paralytic shellfish poisoning, which can cause death. Several species of sea animals, seaweeds, and land plants should be learned and strictly avoided because they are poisonous. All mushrooms should be avoided also.

Be prepared to survive:

- Drink six pints of safe water every day.
- Know several edible plants and animals that can be found in any season.
- Know and avoid poisonous or non-edible plants and animals.

General References

Alaska Department of Environmental Conservation (ADEC). 1983. Alaska's water—Think before you drink. Juneau, Alaska.

Alaska Marine Safety Education Association (AMSEA). 1986. Water and food in the survival situation. Sitka, Alaska.

Angier, B. 1972. Survival with style. Vintage Books, New York.

Barr, L. and N. Barr. 1983. Under Alaskan seas. Alaska Northwest Publishing Company, Anchorage, Alaska.

Carlson, R.E. 1982. Paralytic shellfish poisoning. Cooperative Extension Service, University of Alaska, Fairbanks, Alaska.

Cooperative Extension Service. 1980. Food energy and percentage of U.S. recommended daily allowance for eight nutrients provided by a specific amount of various foods. University of Alaska, Fairbanks, Alaska.

Cooperative Extension Service. 1982. The fisherman returns. University of Alaska, Fairbanks, Alaska.

Cooperative Extension Service. 1985. Wild edible and poisonous plants of Alaska. University of Alaska, Fairbanks, Alaska.

Craighead, F.C. and J.J. Craighead. 1977. How to survive on land and sea. Naval Institute Press, Annapolis, Maryland.

Fears, J.W. 1986. Complete book of outdoor survival. Outdoor Life Books, New York.

Graham, F.K. 1985. Plant lore of an Alaskan island. Alaska Northwest Publishing Co., Anchorage, Alaska.

Gunther, E. 1981. Ethnobotany of western Washington: The knowledge and use of indigenous plants by Native Americans. University of Washington Press, Seattle, Washington.

Hart, J.L. 1980. Pacific fishes of Canada. Bulletin 180. Fisheries Research Board of Canada, Ottawa.

Heller, C.A. and E.M. Scott. 1956-1961. The Alaska dietary survey. U.S. Department of Health, Education and Welfare. Arctic Health Research Center, Anchorage, Alaska.

Hooper, H.M. 1982. Notes on nutrient analysis of several southeast Alaska native foods. Mt. Edgecumbe Hospital, Mt. Edgecumbe, Alaska.

Hooper, H.M. 1984. Nutrient analysis of twenty southeast Alaska native foods. Alaska Native Magazine, Anchorage, Alaska.

Hulten, E. 1968. Flora of Alaska and neighboring territories. Stanford University Press, Stanford, California.

Kessler, D.W. 1985. Alaska's saltwater fishes and other sea life. Alaska Northwest Publishing Co., Anchorage, Alaska.

Kodiak Community College. 1986. Fisheries safety and survival: Shore survival. No. A-2-033. Kodiak, Alaska.

Lamb, A. and P. Edgell. 1986. Coastal fishes of the Pacific Northwest. Harbour Publishing Co. Ltd., Madeira Park, B.C.

McConnaughy, E. 1985. Sea vegetables. Naturegraph Publisher, Inc., Happy Camp, California.

Nettleton, J.A. 1985. Seafood nutrition. Osprey Books, Huntington, New York.

Pill, V. and M. Furlong. 1985. Edible? Incredible! Landover Printing and Graphics, Seattle, Washington.

Robuck, O.W. 1985. The common plants of the muskegs of southeast Alaska. U.S.D.A., Pacific Northwest Forest and Range Experiment Station, Portland, Oregon.

Scagel, R.F. 1967. Guide to common seaweeds of British Columbia. Handbook No. 27. British Columbia Provincial Museum, Victoria, B.C.

Turner, N.J. 1982. Food plants of British Columbia Indians. Handbook No. 34. British Columbia Provincial Museum, Victoria, B.C.

Viereck, E.G. 1987. Alaska's wilderness medicines. Alaska Northwest Publishing Co., Edmonds, Washington.

Walker, M. 1984. Harvesting the northern wild. The Northern Publishers, Yellowknife, N.W.T.

Watt, B.K. and A.L. Merrill. 1975. Composition of foods. Agricultural Handbook No. 8., U.S.D.A. Consumer and Food Economics Institute, Agricultural Research Service, Washington, D.C.

World Health Organization. 1984. Aquatic (marine and freshwater) biotoxins. Environmental Health Criteria 37, Geneva, Switzerland.

APPENDIX: Tables of Nutritional Values of Wild Foods

Table 1. Nutritional value of edible sea animals, per 100 grams.

Name	Reference	Calories	Protein (g)	Fat (g)
Abalone *(Haliotis kamtschatkana)*	CES 1982	98	18.70	0.5
Chiton (gumboots) *(Katharina tunicata)*	Hooper 1984	83	17.10	1.6
Crab, Dungeness *(Cancer magister)*	Watt and Merrill 1975	93	17.30	1.9
Eulachon, raw *(Thaleichthys pacificus)*	Watt and Merrill 1975	118	14.60	6.2
Flounder, baked	Watt and Merrill 1975	202	30.00	8.2
Halibut, Pacific *(Hippoglossus stenolepis)*	Watt and Merrill 1975	171	25.20	7.0
Herring eggs on kelp *(Macrocystis integrifolia)*	Hooper 1984	59	11.30	0.8
Herring eggs, plain *(Clupia harengus pallasi)*	Hooper 1984	56	9.60	1.0
Herring, Pacific *(Clupea harengus pallasi)*	Watt and Merrill 1975	98	17.50	2.6
Needlefish *(Pungitius pungitius)*	Heller and Scott 1956-61		9.90	6.2
Octopus *(Octopus dofleini)*	Hooper 1984	57	11.90	0.6
Pink shrimp	Watt and Merrill 1975	91	18.10	0.8
Salmon, pink raw *(Oncorhynchus gorbuscha)*	Watt and Merrill 1975	119	20.00	3.7
Salmon, sockeye dried *(Oncorhynchus nerka)*	Hooper 1984	371	57.20	14.4
Sea cucumber (yane) *(Parastichopus californicus)*	Hooper 1984	68	13.00	0.4
Smelt *(Osmerus dentex)*	Heller and Scott 1956-61		16.50	5.1
Squid	Watt and Merrill 1975	84	16.40	0.9
Trout, rainbow *(Salmo gairdneri)*	Watt and Merrill 1975	195	21.50	11.4

Vitamin A (IU)	Vitamin C (mg)	Thiamine (mg)	Riboflavin (mg)	Niacin (mg)	Calcium (mg)	Iron (mg)
			0.18	0.14	37	2.40
1650		0.05	0.34	4.20	121	16.00
2170	2.00	0.16	0.08	2.80	43	0.80
			0.04	0.04		
	2.00	0.07	0.08	2.50	23	1.40
53	680.00	0.05	0.07	8.30	16	0.80
89		0.10	0.13	2.70	161	3.40
57	0.60	0.10	0.12	1.80	19	2.70
100	3.00	0.02	0.16	3.50		1.30
1230		0.05	1.38		93	5.00
		0.03	0.04	2.10	24	5.30
		0.02	0.03	3.20	63	1.60
		0.14	0.05			
355	0.02	0.14	0.60	20.20	136	1.90
310		0.05	0.94	3.20	30	0.60
460			0.13	1.50	74	0.60
		0.02	0.12		12	0.50
		0.08	0.20	8.40		

Table 2. Nutritional value of edible wild land plants, per 100 grams.

Name	Reference	Calories	Protein (g)	Fat (g)
Beach asparagus (Salicornia pacifica)	Hooper 1984	27	1.80	0.3
Blueberries (Vaccinium spp.)	Hooper 1984	44	0.70	
Buttercup leaves (Ranunculus pallasi)	Heller and Scott 1956-61		2.50	0.6
Cloudberry (Rubus chamaemorus)	Heller and Scott 1956-61		2.40	0.8
Cranberry	Heller and Scott 1956-61		0.40	0.5
Lady fern (Athyrium filix-femina)	Hooper 1984	34	3.20	0.2
Fireweed leaves (Epilobium latifolium)	Heller and Scott 1956-61		3.00	0.8
Goosetongue (Plantago maritima)	Hooper 1982			
Huckleberry (Vaccinium parvifolium)	Hooper 1984	37	0.40	0.1
Labrador tea (Ledum palustre)	Hooper 1982			
Lingonberry (Vaccinium vitis-idaea)			0.40	0.5
Salmonberry (Rubus spectabilis)	Hooper 1984	44	1.00	0.1
Sitka rose hips (Rosa acicularis)	Hooper 1982			
Sourdock (Rumex arcticus)	Heller and Scott 1956-61		2.30	0.7
Stonecrop (Sedum roseum)	Heller and Scott 1956-61		1.20	1.0
Willow (Salix sp.)	Heller and Scott 1956-61	33	6.10	

Vitamin A (IU)	Vitamin C (mg)	Thiamine (mg)	Riboflavin (mg)	Niacin (mg)	Calcium (mg)	Iron (mg)
1922	1.80	0.01	0.09	0.70	45	0.90
163	2.20	0.03	0.10	0.40	15	1.10
4860		0.04	0.69	1.20	11	2.90
210	158.00	0.05	0.07	0.90	18	0.70
90	21.00	0.02	0.08	0.40	26	0.40
1340	8.90	0.00	0.25	2.00	23	0.80
5720		0.04	0.86	1.40	13	2.10
	2.97			502.50	18	3.20
79	2.80	0.01	0.03	0.30	15	0.31
	0.30			131.80		
90		0.02	0.08	0.40	26	0.40
1550	2.40	0.04	0.07	0.10	14	0.64
	290.99			26.20		
11900	68.00	0.09	0.54	1.10	2	0.80
6250		0.03	0.34	0.80	1	0.60
18700	190.00			2.30	130	2.60

Table 3. Nutritional value of edible sea vegetables, per 100 grams.

Name	Reference	Calories	Protein (g)	Fat (g)
Alaria (Alaria)	McConnaughy 1985		12.70	1.5
Black seaweed, dried (Porphyra sp.)	Hooper 1984	298	28.70	2.0
Bull kelp (Nereocystis)	McConnaughy 1985		7.30	1.1
Dulse, raw (Dilsea edulis)	McConnaughy 1985		25.30	3.2
Laminaria (Laminaria)	McConnaughy 1985		6.50	
Ribbon seaweed, dried (Palmaria palmata)	Hooper 1984	323	19.90	0.6
Sea lettuce (Ulva)	McConnaughy 1985		20.00	
Wakime (Undaria)	McConnaughy 1985		12.00	

Vitamin A (IU)	Vitamin C (mg)	Thiamine (mg)	Riboflavin (mg)	Niacin (mg)	Calcium (mg)	Iron (mg)
140	29.00	0.11	0.14	10.00	1300	13.00
4719	17.40	0.11	2.25	11.50	157	10.40
430	15.00	0.08	0.32	5.70	800	100.00
					567	
430	11.00	0.08	0.32	1.80	800	15.00
23	4.80	0.07	1.00	6.90	190	11.00
960	10.00	0.06	0.03	8.00	730	87.00
140	15.00	0.11	10.00	10.00	1300	13.00

Printed on Recycled Paper
with Soy Based Ink
by Printing Services
University of Alaska Fairbanks